Control or Variable?

D0507277

1. A factor that is changed from sample to sample

2. A factor that is kept the same for all samples tested.

In an experiment, three different colas are offered to subjects in identical glasses and amounts. The subjects taste the colas and choose their favorite.

3. Type of cola

4. Size of glass

5. Amount of cola in glass

2

1. A factor that is changed from sample to sample. - **Variable**

2. A factor that is kept the same for all samples tested. - **Control**

3. Type of cola - **Variable**

4. Size of glass - **Control**

5. Amount of cola in glass - **Control**

Last year, Farmer Jones got a greater yield from Better Bean soybeans than from Super Bean soybeans. This year, Farmer Jones wants to find out if Better Bean plants are really better than Super Bean plants.

Which statement could be a hypothesis for his experiment?

a) Better Bean soybean plants have a longer germination period than Super Bean plants.

b) Farmer Jones should plant with half Better Beans and half Super Beans, then see which kind produces the greater yield.

c) Better Beans produce a greater yield per acre than Super Beans because Better Bean plants have more beans per plant.

The hypothesis, (c), suggests a possible reason for the greater yields, which can be tested by an experiment.

Carbon, nitrogen, and water are constantly cycling through ecosystems. How do plants and animals use each of these elements?

The Carbon Cycle:

Plants absorb carbon dioxide from the air and give off oxygen. Animals inhale oxygen and exhale carbon dioxide. Both plants and animals give off carbon dioxide when they die and decompose.

The Nitrogen Cycle:

Plants absorb nitrogen from the soil. Animals eat plants that contain nitrogen, incorporate nitrogen in their tissues, and excrete excess nitrogen into the soil through their urine.

The Water Cycle:

Water vapor in the atmosphere condenses and then falls on the ground as rain or snow. Plants absorb ground water through their roots and transpire water vapor through their leaves.

The properties of water molecules change based on their state (solid, liquid, or gas).
Label the highest and lowest states for each property in the table.

	Properties		
	Kinetic Energy	Volume	Density
Steam			
Water			
Ice			

	Properties		
	Kinetic Energy	Volume	Density
Steam	Highest	Highest	Lowest
Water		Lowest	Highest
Ice	Lowest		

For this element in the periodic table, determine the

| 11 |
| Sodium |
| **Na** |
| 23 |

\# of protons   = _____

\# of neutrons = _____

\# of electrons = _____

Atomic mass   = _____

Which electron dot diagram is correct?

a) $:O:$ b) $\cdot O \cdot$ c) $:O\cdot$

6

$$\boxed{\begin{array}{c} 11 \\ \text{Sodium} \\ \textbf{Na} \\ 23 \end{array}}$$

# of protons	=	11
# of neutrons	=	12 (23 minus 11)
# of electrons	=	11 (equal to # of protons)
Atomic mass	=	23

b) is the correct dot diagram. $\cdot \overset{\bullet\bullet}{\underset{\bullet\bullet}{0}} \cdot$

Why does an apple stored on a sunny windowsill turn mushy and begin to spoil more quickly than an apple stored in the refrigerator?

As temperature rises, matter will usually change to a more active state. Heat causes the sugar molecules (glucose, sucrose, and fructose) in the apple to break down and, at the same time, increases the activity of bacteria that cause the fruit to spoil.

1. What is the name for a protein molecule that triggers and controls a chemical reaction in a cell?

2. How does this protein molecule lower activation energy to speed up a chemical reaction?

1. Enzyme

2. Enzymes attach themselves to reactant molecules. The enzyme may bring the reactant molecules together in a particular sequence or it may break down the chemical bonds within the molecules, which speeds up the chemical reaction.

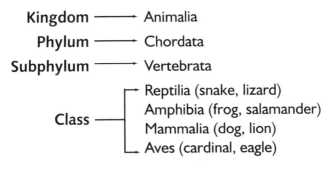

Kingdom ⟶ Animalia

Phylum ⟶ Chordata

Subphylum ⟶ Vertebrata

Class ⟶ Reptilia (snake, lizard)
Amphibia (frog, salamander)
Mammalia (dog, lion)
Aves (cardinal, eagle)

Answer these questions based on the diagram above:

1. True or False? All of the animals listed on the diagram are of subphylum vertebrata.

2. A lizard belongs to what class of animals?

3. Where would you expect a cat to fit into this diagram? Why?

1. True
2. Reptilia
3. Mammalia (similar to a lion)

The five kingdoms of life are bacteria (Monera), protists, fungi, plants, and animals.

1. In which kingdoms are organisms both unicellular and prokaryotic?

2. In which kingdoms do organisms produce their own food through photosynthesis?

1. Bacteria (Monera) are one-celled prokaryotic organisms - the cell has no nucleus. Organisms in the other five kingdoms are eukaryotic, which means that their cells have a nucleus surrounded by a membrane.

2. Plants, some protists, and some bacteria can use the sun's energy to produce their own food energy.

	Bacteria	Protists	Fungi	Plants	Animals
Unicellular	All	Some			
Multicellular			Most	All	All

What are the similarities and differences between plants and animals?

Similarities

- Ability to reproduce
- Respiration systems
- Require water to live
- Living organisms
- Nutrient circulation systems
- Contain carbon
- May be single-celled or multicellular

Differences

Plants

- Lack voluntary locomotion
- Photosynthetic (make food from energy and inorganic materials)
- Cell walls contain cellulose
- Usually rooted in soil, on rocks, or afloat

Animals

- Have voluntary mobility
- Ingest their food; cannot produce it
- Cell walls do not contain cellulose
- Exist on land or water; are not rooted

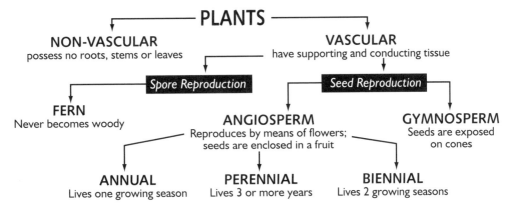

PLANTS

NON-VASCULAR
possess no roots, stems or leaves

VASCULAR
have supporting and conducting tissue

Spore Reproduction

Seed Reproduction

FERN
Never becomes woody

ANGIOSPERM
Reproduces by means of flowers;
seeds are enclosed in a fruit

GYMNOSPERM
Seeds are exposed
on cones

ANNUAL
Lives one growing season

PERENNIAL
Lives 3 or more years

BIENNIAL
Lives 2 growing seasons

What type of plant is:

1. a wild rose bush that has been in the woods for many years
2. a pine tree
3. a carrot (which flowers and produces seeds during its second summer)
4. an apple tree
5. mosses (which distribute water through their bodies by osmosis and diffusion)

12

1. perennial angiosperm
2. gymnosperm
3. biennial angiosperm
4. perennial angiosperm
5. non-vascular

	Has a backbone?	Has a head?	What type of skeleton, if any?
Invertebrates			
Vertebrates			

	Has a backbone?	Has a head?	What type of skeleton, if any?
Invertebrates	No	Sometimes	Some have an exoskeleton
Vertebrates	Yes	Always	All have an endoskeleton

For each beak/feet combination, name a bird that has these characteristics.

Birds' beaks and feet have adapted to allow them to easily get and eat their food. Match each of these beak/feet combinations with the diet that it supports.

Beaks and Feet

1) Sharp beak and curved talons

2) Flat bill and webbed feet

3) Short, strong beak and small feet

Diet

a) Insects that burrow in the mud

b) Small mammals that scurry along the ground

c) Seeds found on plants or on the ground

Beaks and Feet	Diet
1) Birds of prey (hawks)	= b
2) Waterfowl (ducks)	= a
3) Songbirds (sparrows)	= c

How does meiosis ensure genetic
variation from generation to generation?

Meiosis is a special cell division that divides diploid cells into haploid cells called gametes (egg and sperm cells). During fertilization, the egg cell and the sperm cell fuse, and the genes from each parent are combined. This results in an offspring with a genetic make-up that is different from either parent.

The percentages in these diagrams show the concentration of salt in three cells and in the water around each cell.

cell
water

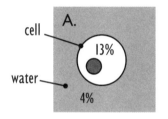
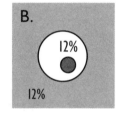
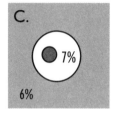

A. 13% 4%

B. 12% 12%

C. 7% 6%

In which two cells will water enter the cell?
What substances are transported by osmosis? By diffusion?

16

Water will enter cells **A** and **C**.

Water is transported by osmosis. Particles dissolved in water are transported by diffusion.

Which is a picture of **cilia** and which is a picture of **flagella**?

A.

B.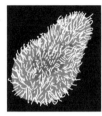

Which of these use cilia or flagella to move?
  1. sperm cell
  2. *E. coli* bacteria
  3. algae
  4. all of the above

17

A. flagella
B. cilia

Flagella are long, hollow organelles that whip back and forth to propel a cell. A large number of short flagella, grouped together tightly, are called cilia. Cilia move like oars.

4. Flagella and cilia are used to move a cell itself or to move a substance over the surface of a cell. Sperm cells, *E. coli* bacteria, and some algae use flagella to move themselves through fluids.

An organelle is a differentiated structure within a cell that performs a specific function. Organelles allow division of labor within the cell. What are the purposes of these cell organelles?

1. nucleus
2. mitochondria
3. chloroplast
4. vacuole
5. ribosome

The largest organelle is the **nucleus**, which controls the activity within a cell.

Mitochondria release the stored energy in food, which was originally created by **chloroplasts**, which make food via photosynthesis.

Vacuoles are plant organelles that store water, nutrients, and waste products. When the plant's vacuoles are full of water, they become rigid; this allows the plant to stand upright. When the vacuoles do not have much water, the plant wilts.

Ribosomes manufacture proteins on the surface of the cellular membrane called the endoplasmic reticulum.

Use the words **tissue** and **organ** to complete this list of body structures, in the correct order from most inclusive to least inclusive.

1. system

2. _____

3. _____

4. cell

1. system
2. organ
3. tissue
4. cell

Cell division occurs either for reproduction or for growth, repair, and maintenance. The two types of cell division are mitosis (where one nucleus splits to form two identical nuclei with the **same** chromosomes) and meiosis (where one nucleus splits to form two nuclei, each of which has **half** of the original cell's chromosomes).

Mitosis or Meiosis?
1. Asexual reproduction
2. Sexual reproduction
3. Hair growth
4. Repair of muscle fibers

1. Asexual reproduction - **Mitosis**

2. Sexual reproduction - **Meiosis**

3. Hair growth - **Mitosis**

4. Repair of muscle fibers - **Mitosis**

The ecosystem of New Zealand developed with mostly birds, insects, and reptiles. Bats were the only mammals there. Since opossums and rabbits were introduced in the 1800's, these non-native species have become a threat to the New Zealand ecosystem. **Explain.**

21

The opossum and rabbit have no natural predators in New Zealand. Both species eat plants to the roots. Both opossums and rabbits have a short breeding cycle, so they can reproduce frequently.

A roller coaster car has _____ energy at **A** and _____ energy at **B**. If there is friction between the car and the track, some of the mechanical energy is transformed into _____ energy. With or without friction, the total energy in the system is _____.

A roller coaster car has **potential energy** at **A** and **kinetic energy** at **B**. If there is friction between the car and the track, some of the mechanical energy is transformed into **thermal** energy. With or without friction, the total energy in the system is **conserved**.

When you ride a bike, it's easier to push on the pedals once you are moving at a constant speed. Use **Newton's laws of motion** to explain why.

Newton's first law of motion: An object at rest (the bike) tends to remain at rest unless acted upon by an outside force (the bike rider). An object in motion tends to stay in motion unless acted upon by an outside force.

1. When you ride a bike, what two factors determine the bike's acceleration? Explain these in terms of **Newton's second law of motion.**

2. What is the formula?

1. **Newton's second law of motion** states, "The net force applied to an object determines the rate of acceleration of that object." The amount of force on the pedals, along with the weight of the bike rider, determines the bike's acceleration. If you push harder on the pedals, the bike will accelerate more quickly. But the more you weigh, the harder you have to push on the pedals to achieve the same acceleration.

2) $F = ma$ Weight = mass (kg) x gravity (9.8 m/s²)

Newton's third law of motion states "For every action, there is an equal and opposite reaction." When you ride a bike, several forces balance each other. What are they?

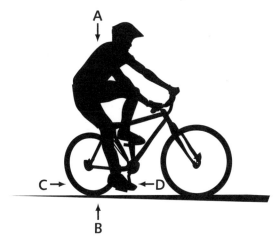

25

A. Your weight plus the weight of the bike

$\quad$ Weight $=$ mass (kg) x gravity (9.8 m/s^2)

B. Normal force

C. Friction from the bike tires against the ground

D. The force you apply to the pedals

1. Why does blood flow at different speeds through large arteries and tiny capillaries?

2. How is the concept of fluid pressure used to determine your blood pressure?

1. The pressure exerted on fluids in motion is constant. Therefore, when blood moves through a large tube like an artery, it moves more slowly than when it is being forced through a tiny tube like a capillary.

2. To measure blood pressure, an inflatable cuff is placed on your upper arm. It is inflated to compress the main artery in your arm until the blood supply is cut off. The person taking your blood pressure uses a stethoscope to listen to the artery. As the cuff is deflated, the blood, which is beginning to flow through the compressed artery under high pressure, causes a tapping sound. At this point, the blood pressure gauge indicates your systolic pressure. When the cuff is deflated even more, the artery is no longer compressed and the tapping sound stops. This is your diastolic pressure.

Choose the right measurement tool for the experiment:
1. Temperature of a liquid
2. Volume of an irregular solid
3. Length of a piece of string
4. Mass of a solid
5. Volume of a liquid

1. Thermometer
2. Graduated cylinder (using displacement)
3. Ruler or meterstick
4. Triple beam balance
5. Graduated cylinder

Match the following elements with the category or series to which they belong.

1. C, N, O, P, S, Se

2. B, Si, Ge, As, Sb, Te, Po

3. He, Ne, Ar, Kr, Xe, Rn

4. All other elements

A) Noble gases

B) Metals

C) Metalloids

D) Nonmetals

1. **D)** Nonmetals - C, N, O, P, S, Se
2. **C)** Metalloids - B, Si, Ge, As, Sb, Te, Po
3. **A)** Noble gases - He, Ne, Ar, Kr, Xe, Rn
4. **B)** Metals - All other elements

Organize the following steps to scientifically solve a problem:

1. Develop a hypothesis.
2. Ask a question based on observations.
3. Draw conclusions.
4. Test hypothesis.
5. Plan test with materials and methods.
6. Do background research.
7. Report findings.
8. Record and analyze data.

2, 6, 1, 5, 4, 8, 3, 7

- Ask a question based on observations.
- Do background research.
- Develop a hypothesis.
- Plan test with materials and methods.
- Test hypothesis.
- Record and analyze data.
- Draw conclusions.
- Report findings.

1. What is the periodic table of elements?

2. Identify the parts of this element square.

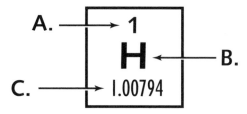

The periodic table of elements is an organizational table developed by Mendeleev in 1869. Elements are arranged in rows by increasing atomic number and in columns by chemical properties.

A. atomic number

B. symbol for element; in this case, hydrogen

C. atomic mass

1. What is a **physical** change in matter? Give examples.

2. What is a **chemical** change in matter? Give examples.

1. A change in the phase (state) of matter or a change in which parts do not lose their identity (**Examples:** ice melting to water; sugar dissolving in water)

2. A reaction that causes a change in the properties of matter; usually difficult to reverse (**Examples:** spilling bleach on a pair of jeans, changing the color; a stick burning in a campfire)

Describe the roles of **producers, consumers, and decomposers** in an ecosystem.

Give an example of each.

Producers make their own food. Plants and algae are producers.

Consumers are organisms that eat other organisms. Animals and protozoans are consumers.

Decomposers break down waste and the remains of dead organisms. Bacteria and fungi are decomposers.

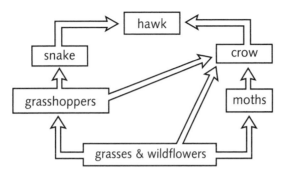

In the prairie food web that is shown, which organism(s) are:

1. primary producers
2. first-order consumers
3. third-order consumers
4. carnivores
5. omnivores

1. grasses & wildflowers
2. grasshoppers, moths, crow
3. hawk
4. snake, hawk
5. crow

1. Which equation summarizes respiration? Which one summarizes photosynthesis?

A) $C_6H_{12}O_6 + 6\,O_2 \rightarrow 6\,CO_2 + 6\,H_2O + energy$

    glucose   oxygen   carbon   water   (ATP)

                                dioxide

B) $6\,CO_2 + 6\,H_2O + energy \rightarrow C_6H_{12}O_6 + 6\,O_2$

    carbon   water   (light)   glucose   oxygen

    dioxide

2. What is the relationship between the processes of respiration and photosynthesis?

1. **A)** respiration
   B) photosynthesis

2. Respiration produces carbon dioxide and water, which are the raw materials used in photosynthesis. The products of photosynthesis (glucose and oxygen) are the raw materials of respiration.

Insect Life Cycles

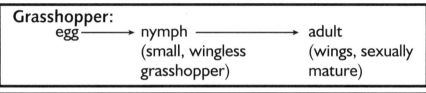

Grasshopper:

egg ⟶ nymph ⟶ adult
(small, wingless grasshopper) (wings, sexually mature)

Moth:

egg ⟶ larva ⟶ pupa ⟶ adult
(caterpillar) (cocoon)

Some insects, such as grasshoppers, undergo _____ metamorphosis in which the immature individual is a miniature version of the adult. Most insects go through a life cycle called _____ metamorphosis that has four distinct stages.

35

Grasshoppers undergo **incomplete metamorphosis**. Moths and most other insects go through a **complete metamorphosis**.

Natural Selection

Suppose a population of small lizards lives on an island of black volcanic rock. The lizards range in color from light gray to dark gray. As birds of prey feed on the lizards, they choose the light gray ones far more often than the dark gray ones. What will most likely happen to the skin color trait in this lizard population over many generations?

In this situation, the dark gray lizards are better adapted for survival. Over time, their numbers will most likely increase while the number of lighter gray lizards will decrease. The accumulation of favorable variations in a population illustrates natural selection.

Red-green colorblindness is a sex-linked inherited trait. It is caused by a recessive gene located on the X chromosome. There is no gene for color vision on the Y chromosome. If C represents the gene for normal color vision and c represents the color-blind gene, the following genotypes are possible:

$X^C X^C$ = female, normal color vision
$X^c X^c$ = female, color-blind
$X^C X^c$ = female, normal color vision, carrier of colorblindness
$X^C Y$ = male, normal color vision
$X^c Y$ = male, color-blind

Mary has normal color vision, but she is a carrier of colorblindness. Her husband Leonard is color-blind. Use a Punnett square or the rules of probability to show the possible genotypes and phenotypes of any children that they could have.

$$X^C X^c \times X^c Y$$

	X^c	Y
X^C	$X^C X^c$	$X^C Y$
X^c	$X^c X^c$	$X^c Y$

Genotypes	Phenotypes
¼ $X^C X^c$	carrier female
¼ $X^c X^c$	color-blind female
¼ $X^C Y$	normal male
¼ $X^c Y$	color-blind male

Tay-Sachs disease is a genetic disorder that results in a breakdown of the nervous system and death at an early age. The disorder is caused by a recessive gene.

In a certain couple, neither parent has Tay-Sachs disease, but each is a carrier of the recessive Tay-Sachs gene. Use a Punnett square to determine the probability of this couple having a child with Tay-Sachs disease.

A = normal gene a = Tay-Sachs gene

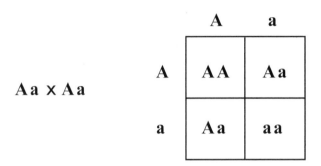

Aa × Aa

	A	a
A	AA	Aa
a	Aa	aa

The probability that this couple could have a child with Tay-Sachs disease (aa) is ¼.

The table shows the genotypes and phenotypes for human blood types.

Genotypes	Phenotypes (blood types)
$I^A I^A$ or $I^A i$	A
$I^B I^B$ or $I^B i$	B
$I^A I^B$	AB
ii	O

1. What term describes the situation in which three or more alleles (I^A, I^B, and i) determine a trait?

2. A person with type AB blood has the alleles I^A and I^B and both are expressed. What term describes this situation in which two dominant alleles are expressed equally?

3. If a person with type O blood marries a person with type AB blood, what blood types are possible among their children?

1. multiple alleles
2. codominance
3. ii × $I^A I^B$

	i	i
I^A	$I^A i$	$I^A i$
I^B	$I^B i$	$I^B i$

The probability of their children having type A blood is ½, and the probability of their children having type B blood is ½.

Active transport or passive transport?

1. Movement is from a region of higher to lower concentration.

2. Transport proteins in the membrane are required.

3. The cell must provide energy.

4. Movement is caused by random molecular movement.

5. Movement is against the concentration gradient.

6. Water enters the cell by this process.

1. Movement is from a region of higher to lower concentration. **Passive transport.**

2. Transport proteins in the membrane are required. **Active transport.**

3. The cell must provide energy. **Active transport.**

4. Movement is caused by random molecular movement. **Passive transport.**

5. Movement is against the concentration gradient. **Active transport.**

6. Water enters the cell by this process. **Passive transport.**

1. Which of the following cell structures is NOT correctly paired with its function(s)?

chloroplast ----- photosynthesis

Golgi apparatus ----- cellular respiration

microtubules ----- structural support; cellular movement

nucleus ----- genetic control center

ribosomes ----- protein synthesis

2. Which cell structures in question 1 are found in both animal cells and plant cells?

1. Golgi apparatus - Its function is to package proteins for secretion. Mitochondria are the sites of cellular respiration.

2. Golgi apparatus, microtubules, nucleus, and ribosomes are features of both animal and plant cells. Chloroplasts are found only in plant cells.

Contrast **prokaryotic** cells and **eukaryotic** cells.

42

Prokaryotic cells do not have DNA enclosed in a nucleus or other membrane-bound organelles. All bacteria are prokaryotes.

Eukaryotic cells have a membrane-bound nucleus that encloses the DNA, plus other membrane-bound organelles. All fungi, protists, plants, and animals are eukaryotes.

Mitosis or Meiosis?

1. Haploid daughter cells

2. Daughter cells are identical

3. Homologous chromosomes form tetrads

4. Two consecutive cell divisions

5. Chromosome number is maintained

6. Produces genetic variation

1. Haploid daughter cells - *Meiosis*

2. Daughter cells are identical - *Mitosis*

3. Homologous chromosomes form tetrads - *Meiosis*

4. Two consecutive cell divisions - *Meiosis*

5. Chromosome number is maintained - *Mitosis*

6. Produces genetic variation - *Meiosis*

Distinguish between **biotic factors** and **abiotic factors** in an organism's environment. List all biotic factors. Give examples of abiotic factors.

Biotic factors are living organisms, and **abiotic factors** are the nonliving factors that affect the organisms in an environment.

Biotic factors are prokaryotes, protists, fungi, plants, and animals. Examples of **abiotic factors** include temperature, water, and light.

Match the following effects on ecosystems to their possible causes:

a) acid precipitation ___ **1.** Habitat destruction

b) biomagnification ___ **2.** Nitrogen and sulfur oxides from power plants and vehicles

c) global warming ___ **3.** Increased levels of atmospheric CO_2

d) loss of biodiversity ___ **4.** Chlorofluorocarbons (CFC's)

e) ozone thinning ___ **5.** Ingestion of pollutants by organisms at the bottom of a food chain

1. d
2. a
3. c
4. e
5. b

Limiting factors keep populations from growing forever. In which of the following situations does the population decline because of a **density-independent limiting factor?** In which is the decline due to a **density-dependent limiting factor?**

1. About 10,000 sea lions live on an island in the Arctic Ocean. Most of them die when a volcano erupts on the island.

2. A herd of antelope lives on a prairie between two mountain ranges. As the population continues to grow, many antelope die from starvation.

1. **Density-independent:** the population decline is caused by an environmental factor unrelated to the size of the population.

2. **Density-dependent:** population growth declines as the density of the antelope population increases. The availability of food is directly related to the size of the population.

Energy Pyramid

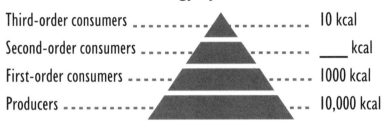

Third-order consumers	10 kcal
Second-order consumers	_____ kcal
First-order consumers	1000 kcal
Producers	10,000 kcal

1. At which level is the most energy available? Which level has the least available energy?

2. How many kilocalories of energy are available to the organisms at the second-order consumers trophic level?

3. At which trophic level would the organisms have the greatest total biomass?

1. The producer level has the most energy. The third-order consumer level has the least.

2. 100 kcal

3. Producers. Since only about 10% of the energy transfers up to the next higher trophic level, a large amount of biomass is needed at the base of a food chain to support a few organisms at upper trophic levels.

mRNA codons	amino acids
AGC	serine
GAA	glutamic acid
GUA	valine
UUU	phenylalanine

Suppose a section of mRNA that reads **UUUGAAAGC** becomes mutated to **UUUGUAAGC**.
Explain what would happen and why mutations occur.

48

The mutated mRNA would cause the amino acid valine to be substituted for glutamic acid in the resulting protein. Mutations are often caused by exposure to environmental agents. A mutation can also be caused by a spontaneous chemical change in a gene.

1. DNA is composed of building blocks called nucleotides. Name the three parts of a nucleotide.

2. Describe the double helix model of DNA.

3. What is the function of the DNA molecule?

1. A nucleotide is composed of a five carbon sugar (deoxyribose), a phosphate group, and a nitrogen-containing base.

2. The double helix resembles a twisted ladder. The sides are formed by alternating sugars and phosphate groups. The steps are made of pairs of nitrogen bases held together by hydrogen bonds.

3. DNA stores coded genetic information that tells cells the precise sequence of amino acids needed to produce proteins.

1. Define a wave.

2. Name some types of waves.

3. Which type does not need matter to travel?

4. What is interference?

5. Name the two types of interference shown here.

a)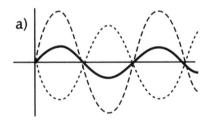

b)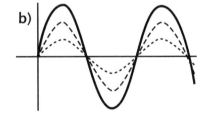

1. A wave is a traveling disturbance that transfers energy from one place to another.

2. Some types of waves include sound, seismic, water, and light waves.

3. Light waves do not need matter to travel.

4. Interference occurs when two waves pass through the same space at the same time.

5. Constructive interference (**b**) means that two waves are "in phase" - their crests and troughs are in sync. Destructive interference (**a**) occurs when the two waves are out of phase.

Dear Parents,

Here's how to use these flashcards to help your child prepare for the **AHSGE:**

- Use the flashcards regularly. Practice 15-30 minutes each night for several weeks before the test.

- Discuss the flashcards. New discoveries in science have led to many changes in the content that is taught in science class. If some of the information is unfamiliar to you, ask your child to explain some of the new content. Offer real-life examples of the terms and ideas that are familiar to you.

- Make a check mark on a flashcard each time your child answers that card correctly. After several sessions look for flashcards with no (or few) checkmarks. Discuss these with your child and seek help from the teacher for these skills.

- Read the advice to the students on the reverse side of this card and urge your child to follow it.

Dear Student,
Here are some
ideas to help you
on the **AHSGE:**

- Practice reading graphs, tables, and
diagrams. Use examples in your science
textbook for practice. Many questions
on the test require that you read a
graph, table, or diagram, so it is very
important to practice.

- Talk to your teacher at least two weeks
before the test if you need help with any
of the terms or ideas on your flashcards.

- Read the test carefully. Don't just skim.
Read the question and all responses
before you answer.

- Take your time and check your work.

- Come to the test rested and ready.

Remember to study your Flashcards for
15 - 30 minutes every day for a few
weeks before the test.

© 2005
Hollandays
Publishing
Corporation

ISBN 0-9753239-4-6

US $7.95